DRAW
THE VERSE

A Scripture Memory & Application Tool for Families

Julie Parido

Illustrated by Alissa Bercaw

KW
KingdomWinds
PUBLISHING

First Edition, 2022
ISBN 978-1-64590-029-0
Published by Kingdom Winds Publishing.
www.kingdomwinds.com
publishing@kingdomwinds.com
Printed in the United States of America.

TABLE OF CONTENTS

INTRODUCTION

DEAR PARENTS,

Welcome to *Draw the Verse*! I hope you find this unique book beneficial for scripture memory, gospel-centered application, and intentional discipleship time with your children. God has gifted you with the high calling of teaching your children about Him, which can sometimes feel overwhelming. Therefore, I created this book to help parents teach their children scripture in a fun and effective way. (Please note: While the book is designed for parents and children to complete together, older children could go through it independently.)

As you go through the book, you and your children will draw visual representations of Bible memory verses. Research has proven that drawing is an excellent way to memorize information. As a parent, I can attest that drawing the actual pictures that scripture describes helps imprint those images into kids' (and their parents') hearts and minds, aiding in scripture memorization.

There are 24 memory verses in this book, and I recommend completing one verse per week. Each memory verse comes with two copies of the same illustration for you and your children to utilize—one next to the text and one in the back of the book. There is also a website address on the next page to download more copies of the illustrations if you have multiple children, want to go through the book a second time, mess up the original drawing, etc.

The information for the verses is broken up into the sections below. You will read each section aloud to your children as you go through the book:

MEMORIZE IT!   This section introduces you to the scripture verse. You should aim to memorize the verse with your children and will draw it in the next step.

DRAW IT!   You and your children will follow the instructions to add your unique drawings to the illustrations to create a visual representation of the memory verse. (You may find your children getting enthusiastic about their drawings, which is great! If this is the case, you may want to read the remaining sections after they are done drawing and have settled down a bit.)

LEARN IT!   This section explains what the verse means.

DISCUSS IT!   The questions in this section will help you engage in conversation with your children and ensure comprehension of the verse. You should feel free to answer the questions as well.

LIVE IT! In this section, you and your children will discover how you can practically live out what you learned from the verse and will be prompted to pray together.

STUDY IT! Here you will find passages of scripture for further study and encouragement related to the memory verse. This section is optional. If you want to dig deeper into the topics discussed in the previous sections, you and your children can look up these scripture passages together.

After completing these sections, I recommend displaying your children's drawing pages on your refrigerator or somewhere else where they can be easily seen. I encourage you to take time throughout the week to talk about the picture, recite the verse, and review the related sections as needed.

My prayer is that by the time you and your children finish this book, you will be able to visualize the memory verses you drew and be encouraged through the corresponding application sections to live out those verses. I hope you enjoy quality time with your children as you go through this book and draw near to God—together!

Happy drawing!

Julie Parido, author

Download additional copies of *Draw the Verse* illustrations here:

https://kingdomwinds.com/draw-the-verse-download/

Memorize It!

"The heavens declare the glory of God; the skies proclaim the work of his hands."

Psalm 19:1 (NIV)

6

DRAW IT! Wow! You're an astronaut in outer space! Draw your face inside the astronaut's helmet. Also, add some "out of this world" objects to the picture. Some things you might want to include are stars, planets, and the moon.

LEARN IT! Have you ever looked up at the sky on a dark, cloudless night? You should've been able to see plenty of twinkling stars, the glowing moon, and maybe even a distant planet. The sky is an incredible sight to see!

Psalm 19:1 tells us that outer space is actually a work of God's hands—it's His own personal artwork! Just like you take a blank piece of paper and draw your own picture on it, God took the blank sky and filled it with His very own design. The sky helps us see how great and awesome He is.

Who else but a great God could set the sun and moon in just the right spots so people, plants, and animals can live on the earth? Who else but a great God could create a huge number of stars, planets, and galaxies just to show how wonderful and powerful He is?

DISCUSS IT! What's the most interesting thing you've ever seen in the sky? How does that thing show God's glory or greatness? Why do you think the verse talks about God's glory being seen through the "heavens" and not another part of His creation like the mountains, animals, or oceans?

LIVE IT! Let's take some time this week to study the sky during the day and night. You can write down everything you see, such as storm clouds, the blazing sun, or a full moon. At the end of the week, let's thank God for making such a detailed sky that shows His greatness!

What's your favorite part of outer space? Let's pray now and thank God for creating a sky that points us to His glory.

STUDY IT! To learn more about how God created and controls the objects in the sky, read Job 38:22-35. Also, check out Psalm 147:4. Did you know God has a name for every star?

Memorize It!

"When I remember you on my bed, I meditate on you in the night watches, for you have been my help, and in the shadow of your wings I sing for joy."

Psalm 63:6-7 (NASB)

WEEK 2

DRAW IT! Imagine this is a picture of your bedroom. What special things would be in the picture? Draw yourself sleeping in the bed with your favorite blanket. Add things from your room like stuffed animals, toys, and furniture.

LEARN IT! King David, the writer of Psalm 63, slept in lots of different places throughout his life, from the best palaces during his time as king to deep, dark caves hiding from his enemies. As a king, he probably had many important things to think about while lying in bed at night. But King David learned that thinking about God while he rested in bed was the best choice. Psalm 63 tells us that David thought about God "in the watches of the night." This means that he thought about God throughout the night. That's a long time to think about one thing!

What thoughts do you think were going through his mind? Psalm 63:7 gives us a few clues. It says that God was David's helper, so David was probably remembering times when God had helped him. Verse 7 also says that David sang to God, so there's a good chance he was thinking of his favorite worship songs and praising God with them while he lay in bed.

DISCUSS IT! What do you usually think about while you lie in bed at night? How can you remember God at night as David did?

LIVE IT! While we rest in bed, it's easy to let our minds wander. Let's learn from King David and set our minds on God before we fall asleep. Like David, we can remember how God helped us in the past, or we can think through our favorite worship song. We can also think through scripture verses we are memorizing (like the verses in this book) or praise God for His creation.

Let's pray together now, asking God to help us get in the habit of thinking about Him before we fall asleep, just like David did.

STUDY IT! For more encouragement to set your mind on God and His Word at night (and during the day), check out Psalm 1.

Memorize It!

"The path of the righteous is like the morning sun, shining ever brighter till the full light of day. But the way of the wicked is like deep darkness; they do not know what makes them stumble."

Proverbs 4:18-19 (NIV)

DRAW IT! Oh no! You're trapped in a dark cave! Draw yourself inside the cave. Add some animals that you might find inside a cave, like bats, insects, and bears.

LEARN IT! It would be scary to be stuck in a dark cave. Proverbs 4:18-19 teaches us that the way wicked people live is like being trapped in deep darkness. They need a light to find their way out.

Apart from God's Son, Jesus, we're all trapped in "deep darkness" because our sin separates us from God. ("Sin" is a Bible word that means breaking God's rules.) The good news is that God sent Jesus to rescue us from the darkness. Jesus is the way out of the darkness of sin and the way to a relationship with God. (To learn more about following Jesus out of darkness, check out the "Study it!" section.)

After following Jesus out of darkness, we will be on the "path of the righteous," which means the way taken by those who follow God. Walking on the "path of the righteous" is like walking on a trail outside in the early morning sun. As the sun rises in the sky, we can clearly see what's around us. Similarly, we won't be trapped in darkness when we're living a righteous life. We'll be walking a clear path, knowing exactly where to go.

DISCUSS IT! Where's the darkest place you've been? What is the way of the wicked (those who aren't following Jesus) compared to in the verse? What's the way out of deep darkness? What is the "path of the righteous" compared to in the verse?

LIVE IT! Following Jesus means turning from your sin and growing in your love for God by reading the Bible to gain wisdom and obeying what it says with the help of God's Spirit. When you follow Jesus, you'll see the sin you should stay away from and the right path you should follow.

Let's pray together now, thanking Jesus for providing the way out of the darkness of sin.

STUDY IT! If you or your child have never decided to follow Jesus to the path of the righteous, check out these verses (often referred to as "The Romans Road to Salvation") to get a complete picture of the good news Jesus offers us: Romans 3:10-24; Romans 6:23; Romans 5:8; Romans 10:9-13; Romans 5:1-2; and Romans 8:1.

Memorize It!

"You are my hiding place; you will protect me from trouble and surround me with songs of deliverance."

Psalm 32:7 (NIV)

DRAW IT!
Look at the picture of the treehouse. If this were your very own hiding place, what would you want to have in it to make it special? Would you want some favorite stuffed animals, books, or toys? Add your favorite things to the picture. You can also add some fluffy clouds to the sky, green leaves to the tree, and birds to the picture if you'd like!

LEARN IT!
When we disobey (which is another word for "sin"), it's easy to feel embarrassed, isn't it? We may want to hide our sin from others and maybe even from God. King David is the writer of Psalm 32:7. Like us, he felt guilty and ashamed when he sinned. *(For full context, read Psalm 32:1-11.)*

Psalm 32 doesn't tell us what King David's sin was, just that he tried to hide his sin from God. Finally, he told God about his sin, and God forgave him. God didn't stop at forgiving Him, though. He also showed David that he could find protection in Him, just as if God was David's own safe hiding place.

After confessing his sin, David wrote Psalm 32:7, "You are my hiding place; you will protect me from trouble and surround me with songs of deliverance." Deliverance in this verse means "escape." David understood that when he sins, he shouldn't escape *from* God; he should escape *to* God.

DISCUSS IT!
Where do you like to go for safety and comfort after you've messed up? Do we need to hide from God when we disobey Him? What does it mean that God is our hiding place? What does deliverance mean, and why do you think we need it?

LIVE IT!
God is a hiding place for us, just like He was for David. When we sin against God, we can run to Him for forgiveness and protection. He wants to be our place of safety.

Let's pray now, thanking God for being our hiding place and asking Him to help us always escape to Him. Don't we serve a good God?

STUDY IT!
Check out the book of Jonah to discover what happened to Jonah when he ran from God instead of running to God.

Memorize It!

"When you pass through the waters, I will be with you; and when you pass through the rivers, they will not sweep over you... For I am the Lord your God, the Holy One of Israel, your Savior."

Isaiah 43:2a, 3a (NIV)

WEEK 5

DRAW IT! Look at that rushing water! Can you imagine trying to get across it safely? Draw yourself and some friends walking through the water. Add some surrounding plants, trees, and animals too.

LEARN IT! It would be scary to walk through a big river, don't you think? Large fish could get too close to us, or the rushing water may sweep us further down the river than we want to go.

In these verses, God was speaking to His people, the Israelites. He was telling them that they would have challenging things they'd have to go through. God knew they would feel afraid, and He promised to be with them. And not only that, but He reminded them that, even though there would be some scary times ahead, He was in control of their future. He reminded them that they could trust Him.

When you have decided to follow Jesus, God promises to care for you, just like He cared for the Israelites! You can trust that wherever you go, whatever you do, God is with you, just like He was with them.

DISCUSS IT! Why might it be scary to swim across a flowing river? Who is God speaking to in these verses? What did God promise the Israelites? Who is in control of your future?

LIVE IT! God will never break a promise. We can trust Him completely! Let's keep a running list of God's promises that are ours once we decide to follow Him. Here are a few promises to get us started: Nothing will separate us from God's love (Romans 8:31-39), Jesus is always with His followers (Matthew 28:20), and God is our comforter (2 Corinthians 1:3-5). Let's add to this list as we discover other promises in the Bible.

Let's pray together now, thanking God for always being with us, just like He was with the Israelites in our verses.

STUDY IT! To learn more about God being with people during difficult times, check out Daniel 3.

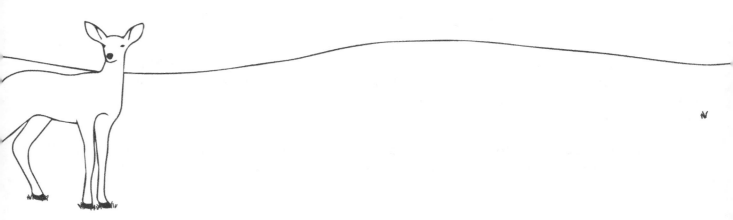

MEMORIZE IT!

"A deer longs for streams of water. God, I long for you in the same way."

Psalm 42:1 (NIRV)

DRAW IT! This deer needs a forest to live in and some fresh water to drink. Draw some water in front of the deer. It can be a lake, stream, river—whatever you'd like! Also, add some flowers, trees, and grass to the picture.

LEARN IT! Can you think back to the last time you played outside on a hot summer day? It probably didn't take long before you were sweaty, tired, and thirsty. You couldn't wait to get a drink to help you cool down! Just like you, the deer in Psalm 42:1 really wanted fresh water. Once the deer drank water from the stream—just like once you got your cool drink on that hot day—it felt happy and ready to continue on its way...for a while. Pretty soon, it would be thirsty for water again.

David, the writer of Psalm 42:1, had a thirst for God, just like your body and the deer in our verse have a thirst for water. Praying to God and reading His Word every once in a while was not enough for David. He wanted to be with God every day!

DISCUSS IT! Who is your best friend? Why do you like to spend time with him or her? Who did David want to spend time with? How does David wanting to be with God compare to a deer wanting water?

LIVE IT! If we're going to want God just like a deer wants water, then we have to spend time with Him! We won't grow closer to someone we're not spending time with.

We spend time with God by praying to Him, worshipping Him, and reading His Word, the Bible. Let's get into the habit of praying, worshipping, and reading our Bibles every day. Maybe we could even do these things together.

Spending time with God will help us want Him as David did, but it's easy to get distracted and lose our focus on God, letting other things become more important than Him. Let's ask God now to help us want Him as much as the deer in Psalm 42:1 wanted water.

STUDY IT! To learn more about desiring God and His Word, check out Psalm 19:7-11 and Philippians 3:7-11.

Memorize It!

"My sheep listen to my voice. I know them, and they follow me."

John 10:27 (NIRV)

WEEK 7

DRAW IT! That shepherd needs a flock of sheep to care for! Draw some fluffy white sheep in the picture. Add some green rolling hills, trees, and flowers to the picture as well.

LEARN IT! Did you know that sheep need a shepherd? It's true! Sheep need someone to guide and protect them. Without a shepherd, they would easily wander away and get attacked by other animals.

Just like sheep, we need a shepherd to guide and protect us. That person is Jesus! Once we have decided to follow Jesus, He promises to lead us faithfully like a shepherd. Our job as His sheep is to listen to and follow Him.

Not only does John 10:27 tell us that Jesus' true sheep will listen to Him and follow Him in obedience, but it also teaches us that Jesus knows His sheep. Isn't that amazing? God, who made the stars and the oceans, knows each and every one of His sheep. Take comfort in that truth today!

DISCUSS IT! Have you ever played "follow the leader?" What do you have to be doing to play the game well? What does it mean that Jesus' sheep follow Him? How is Jesus like a shepherd to His followers? What do you think it means for Jesus to "know" His sheep?

LIVE IT! It's easy to drown out God's voice with the sounds of the world around us. Video games, television shows, and friends all scream for our attention and easily distract us. But John 10:27 says that Jesus' sheep, first and foremost, listen to His voice. To follow Him, we need to be sure we're listening to Him. As you read your Bible, pay attention to what God is telling you in it, and follow Him in the way He wants you to go!

Let's pray together, asking God to help us listen to His voice and follow Him in obedience.

STUDY IT! To understand why we can trust that the Bible is God's way of speaking to His followers, check out 2 Timothy 3:16-17. To learn more about what it means to actively follow God, read James 1:21-25. Finally, check out Psalm 23 to read more about Jesus being a shepherd to His followers.

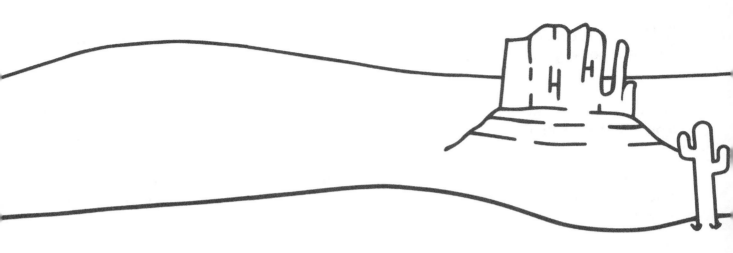

MEMORIZE IT!

"This is what the LORD says: 'Cursed is the man who trusts in mankind and makes flesh his strength, and whose heart turns away from the LORD. For he will be like a bush in the desert, and will not see when prosperity comes."

Jeremiah 17:5-6a (NASB)

DRAW IT! This sandy desert looks super hot and dry. What other desert animals and objects do you think would be in a place like this? Draw how you'd imagine a desert to look. You can add another cactus and more animals like jackrabbits, scorpions, and snakes. Be sure to include a bush and a scorching sun!

LEARN IT! Can you imagine someone actually planting a bush in the hot, dry desert? It would have very little water and no escape from the blazing sun. Its leaves would quickly become brown, lifeless, and crunchy. It certainly wouldn't grow any fruit!

Jeremiah 17:5-6a tells us that people who turn their hearts away from God are just like the bushes in our desert pictures. (The word "hearts" in the Bible usually means our thoughts, wants, and feelings—not the hearts inside our bodies.) People who trust in their own thoughts, wants, and feelings, instead of trusting God, are not spiritually strong and healthy. They don't have the things they need to grow, just like a bush planted in the desert.

Our hearts naturally turn away from God. Our hearts cannot be trusted. That's why it's important for us to compare our thoughts, wants, and feelings to God's Word, the Bible, to make sure we are believing what the Bible says is true.

DISCUSS IT! What words would you use to describe a desert? What does the word "heart" mean in the Bible? How is a bush in a desert similar to a person who turns his heart away from the Lord?

LIVE IT! We don't want to be like bushes trying to grow in the desert. Let's pray together now, asking God to show us if anything we think, want, or feel doesn't match what His Word says is true or good. Let's ask Him to help us always keep our hearts turned toward Him.

STUDY IT! Read Proverbs 3:5-6 to learn more about Who you should trust. (Also, check out next week's memory verse!)

Memorize It!

"Blessed is the man who trusts in the Lord, and whose trust is the Lord. For he will be like a tree planted by the water that extends its roots by a stream, and does not fear when the heat comes; but its leaves will be green, and it will not be anxious in a year of drought, nor cease to yield fruit."

Jeremiah 17:7-8 (NASB)

DRAW IT! This stream looks so calm and peaceful. The land beside it would be the perfect spot for a tree. Draw a big tree near the water. Give it a strong, thick trunk! Add roots that go out of the bottom of the trunk and into the water. Draw some bright green leaves and fruit on the tree's branches.

LEARN IT! How does your tree drawing look? The tree seems steady and secure, right? It has its roots stretched out to the water and appears to be growing strong. If bad weather came to a tree like that, it wouldn't dry up or get blown over.

A tree that's always growing no matter the weather sounds impossible, but God says we can be exactly like that kind of tree. When the "roots" of our hearts are stretched out to God, "soaking up" His Word and trusting Him, He will give us everything we need to handle the "bad weather" in life, like when we have a rough day or don't get what we want.

We won't be fearful of life's "storms" when we're regularly trusting God. We can depend on Him in every season of life. And when we depend on God, we'll be just like the trees in our pictures—strong and unafraid.

DISCUSS IT! Why is it important for trees to get plenty of water? How is the tree in the verse described? How is a person who trusts in God like a tree planted near water?

LIVE IT! I want to be just like the trees in our pictures, don't you? Let's ask God now to help us trust Him, so we can be growing strong no matter if the "weather" in our life is good or bad.

STUDY IT! To learn more about depending on God during life's difficulties, read 2 Corinthians 1:1-11. To study how the Holy Spirit helps followers of Jesus trust in and obey Him, read John 14:15-27.

Memorize It!

"Therefore everyone who hears these words of mine and puts them into practice is like a wise man who built his house on the rock...
But everyone who hears these words of mine and does not put them into practice is like a foolish man who built his house on sand."

Matthew 7:24, 26 (NIV)

24

WEEK 10

DRAW IT! Imagine a windy thunderstorm just passed through the picture. Draw what the picture would look like after the storm passed through. Be sure to include a strong house on the rock that's unaffected by the storm and a tumbling-down house on the sand.

LEARN IT! A house built on a rock is strong and secure. Floodwaters, rain, and wind wouldn't knock it down. But a house built on sand is shaky. It would quickly fall during bad weather. The sand beneath it would move around, causing the house to crumble.

Matthew 7:24 and 26 teach us that a person who hears and obeys God's Word is just like the house on the rock we drew. He's not going to fall apart during life's "storms." Knowing and obeying God's Word keeps him steady, safe, and strong.

However, if a person hears God's Word and doesn't obey it, he'll be like the house built on sand. He'll be weak and shaky, and he'll quickly fall apart when life gets tough.

DISCUSS IT! Why is it better to live in a house built on rock instead of a house built on sand? How is a person who hears God's Word and obeys it like a house built on rock? How is a person who hears God's Word but doesn't obey it like a house built on sand?

LIVE IT! It's not always easy to follow God's ways, but if we want to be like that house on the rock, we must study God's Word and obey it. God doesn't just want outward obedience; He wants to change us on the inside by making our thoughts and wants more like His. As we let Him change us on the inside, the outward obedience will follow, and we'll be just like the house on the rock—strong and steady no matter what comes our way.

Let's pray now, asking God to make our hearts like His and for His help to obey what the Bible says.

STUDY IT! To learn more about the importance of following God's wise ways, check out Proverbs 3.

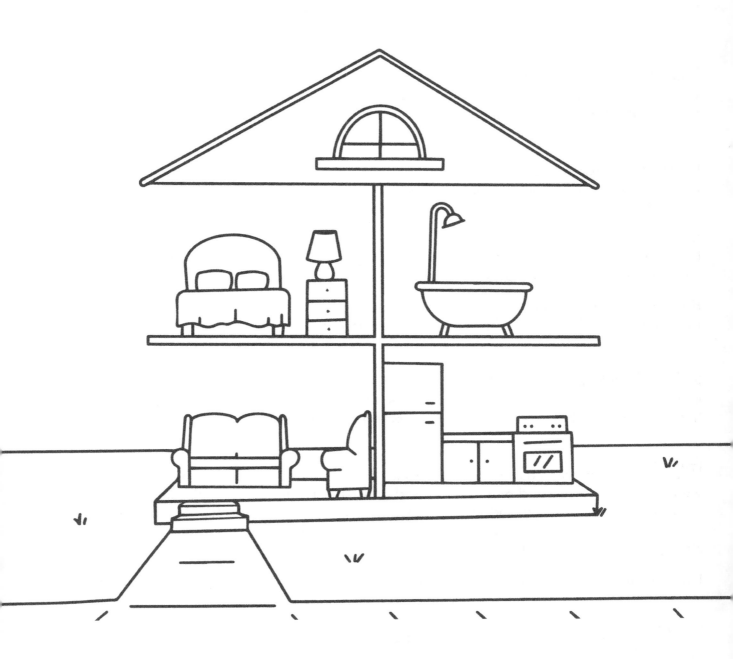

MEMORIZE IT!

"A man without self-control is like a city broken into and left without walls."
Proverbs 25:28 (ESV)

DRAW IT! In Bible times, cities were surrounded by tall, strong walls. You don't live in a city with walls, but you do live in a house with walls. Look at the picture of the house with no walls. What would happen to a house like that? Wild animals and bad weather would certainly get inside it!

Draw some animals from your neighborhood that would be inside your house if it didn't have walls. What kind of weather do you experience where you live? Do you get lots of snow, rain, or heat? Add some bad weather to the picture as well.

LEARN IT! How would you feel if you lived inside the house you just drew? You definitely wouldn't be protected very well in a house without walls! It would be dangerous and noisy. There wouldn't be anything keeping wild animals and loud noises out of it. Could you imagine trying to sleep during a thunderstorm in a house with no walls?

Proverbs 25:28 says that a person without self-control is just like the house in the picture. Self-control is the ability to control your words, thoughts, and actions. The "walls" of self-control protect us from doing whatever we feel like doing, just like the walls of our house protect us from dangers outside of the house. When the "walls" of self-control are removed, people open themselves up to go through troubles God wants to guard or protect them from.

DISCUSS IT! What kinds of things do you think you would see, hear, and feel if our house didn't have walls? How is a person without self-control like a house without walls?

LIVE IT! We all have times when we feel like being out of control with our words, thoughts, and actions. But if we want to be protected like a house with walls, we need to be self-controlled. Let's ask God now to give us self-control so that we can be just like a house with walls—safe and secure!

STUDY IT! To learn more about self-control, read Titus 2:11-12. Also, check out Matthew 4:1-10 and notice the tool that Jesus used to fight temptation and remain self-controlled was scripture, just like you and your children are memorizing in this book!

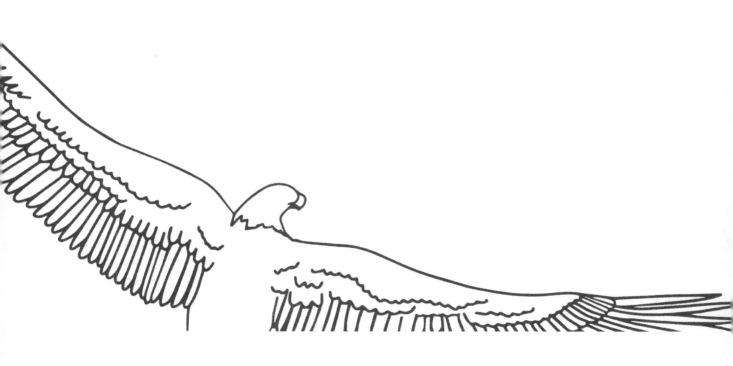

Memorize It!

"Even youths grow tired and weary, and young men stumble and fall; but those who hope in the Lord will renew their strength. They will soar on wings like eagles; they will run and not grow weary, they will walk and not be faint."

Isaiah 40:30-31 (NIV)

WEEK 12

DRAW IT! This eagle is soaring high in the sky. Draw yourself on the wings of the eagle. Are you flying over the mountains? Desert? Ocean? Add your favorite landscape to the earth below.

LEARN IT! Can you imagine how an eagle must feel to soar above the ground beneath him? He can quickly escape danger by flying high up into the air. Isaiah 40:30-31 teaches us that God will give us strength like an eagle when we hope in Him.

To hope in something means you want that good thing to happen in your future. Maybe you hope you can play with your friends today or eat pizza for dinner tonight. These types of hopes will make your life a little better for a while, but God offers us a never-ending hope—hope in Him and His promises! When we look to God and His promises when life gets tough, He will make us strong and help us "soar" above the hard parts of life, just like an eagle.

DISCUSS IT! What does hope mean? What's something you hope will happen this week? What's the difference between hoping to eat pizza for dinner and hoping in God?

LIVE IT! Sometimes life can be really hard, right? When we have difficult days, we can get new strength by hoping in God. We hope in God by focusing on the truths of the Bible, like God will always love us (Ephesians 3:17-19), we will see Him one day if we are His followers (John 3:16), His character will never change (Malachi 3:6, Hebrews 13:8), and God will only do what's best for His followers (Romans 8:28-29).

Let's pray together now, asking God to help us hope in Him and His promises when we have hard days.

STUDY IT! For more context for these verses, check out Isaiah 40:27-29. Read Hebrews 11:13-16, 1 Peter 1:1-9, and Psalm 42 to learn more about hoping in God.

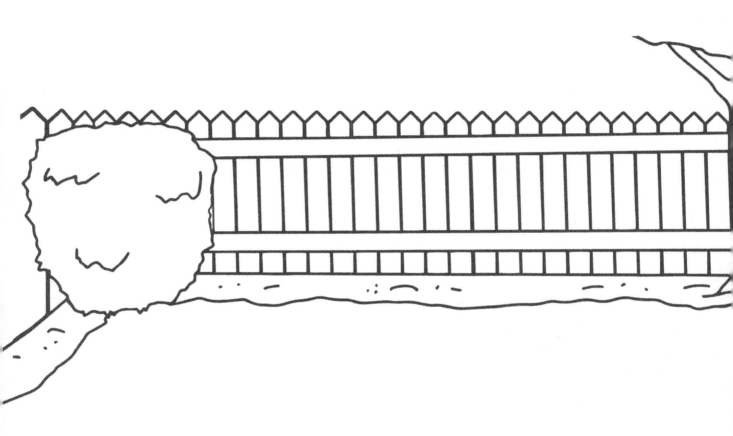

Memorize It!

"A gentle answer turns anger away. But mean words stir up anger."

Proverbs 15:1 (NIRV)

WEEK 13

DRAW IT! Imagine there's a strong wind storm blowing through the picture, making a mess of the backyard. Draw what the picture would look like after the storm passes through. There would probably be a mess of branches, leaves, and dirt. Add those things to the picture. You can also include any other small objects that are in your yard that might get blown around by a strong wind. (Do you have a small dog or neighborhood cat that might get easily blown away? Yikes!)

LEARN IT! Have you ever seen stuff in your yard get blown around on a windy day? A strong breeze usually picks up whatever is in its path and can make neighborhoods messy very quickly.

Just like the wind stirs up things on the ground, we also stir up good or bad feelings inside people just by the words we choose to say. For example, imagine a brother and sister are playing a board game together, and the sister wins the game. The brother may feel frustrated and want to say mean words to her. But according to Proverbs 15:1, mean words would stir up angry feelings inside of his sister, just like the wind stirred up objects in your backyard drawing.

On the other hand, speaking gentle words turns away anger. Gentle words are sweet, kind, and loving. Instead of saying mean words to his sister about the game, he could say, "You did a great job. Let's play again!" Speaking this way would show love to his sister and bring peace to the relationship.

DISCUSS IT! What does the verse say is the result of speaking gentle words? What is the result of speaking mean words? Would you prefer someone to say gentle or mean words to you? Why?

LIVE IT! We don't want to stir up angry feelings inside of anyone by speaking meanly. Let's pray together now and ask God to help us speak gentle words, not mean words, when we feel overwhelmed, angry, or irritated.

STUDY IT! A man named Joseph spoke gently to his brothers after they treated him badly. Check out Genesis 50:15-21 to read what he said to them.

MEMORIZE IT!

"At one time my heart was sad and my spirit was bitter. I didn't have any sense.
I didn't know anything. I acted like a wild animal toward you.
But I am always with you. You hold me by my right hand."

Psalm 73:21-23 (NIRV)

32

DRAW IT! That jungle needs some animals in it! Draw some jungle creatures, like gorillas, elephants, or snakes.

LEARN IT! Animals can be fun to see at the zoo when they're safely behind a cage. But if you were to run into one of those animals in the wild, you'd better watch out! When animals are not used to being around humans, there's no telling what they might do to you.

Asaph, the writer of Psalm 73, knew a thing or two about wild animals. In fact, he compared himself to a wild animal! Asaph says about himself, "I didn't have any sense. I didn't know anything. I acted like a wild animal toward you." In other words, he was thinking and acting like a crazy person! Why do you think that was the case? Verse 21 tells us it was because his "heart was sad" and his "spirit was bitter." Something had happened to him that made him very sad and hurt, and because of that, he acted foolishly toward God, like a wild animal.

How would you respond if someone acted like a wild animal toward you? You probably wouldn't want to stick around that person! But do you know how God responded to Asaph? He stayed right with him!

God will never leave us when we are struggling with life's difficulties. He's right there with us, ready to comfort, love, and guide us. All we have to do is turn to Him like Asaph did.

DISCUSS IT! What's your favorite animal? How might that animal act in the wild? Have you ever acted like a wild animal when you were frustrated, angry, or disappointed?

LIVE IT! Are there any difficult feelings or situations you're struggling with now? We can be honest with God about how hard life can sometimes be. Let's pray now, thanking God for His faithfulness to us and letting Him know about anything that might be bothering us.

STUDY IT! To get the full context of the verses, read all of Psalm 73. To learn more about God never leaving His followers, check out Romans 8:35-39.

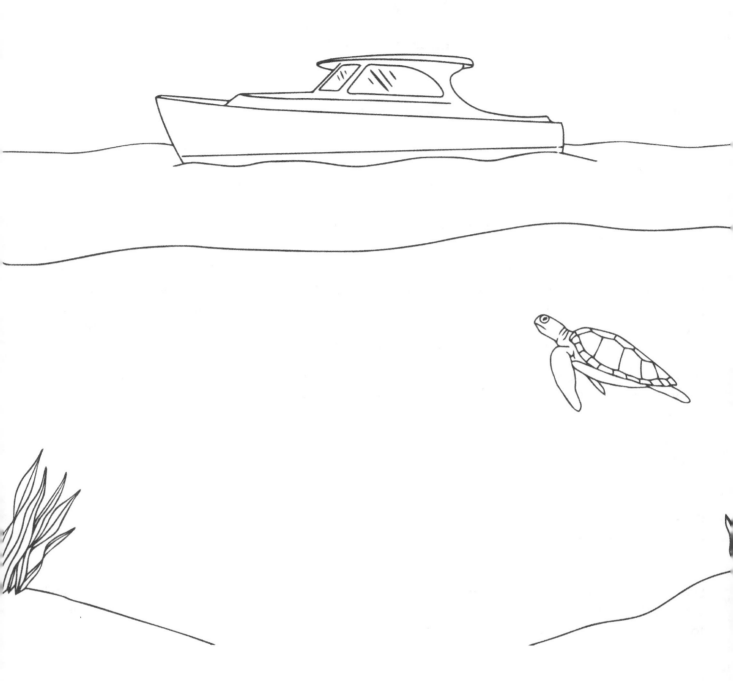

Memorize It!

"Then they cried out to the Lord because of their problems. And he brought them out of their troubles. He made the storm as quiet as a whisper. The waves of the ocean calmed down."

Psalm 107:28-29 (NIRV)

DRAW IT! Imagine this boat is floating in the ocean on a nice, sunny day. Draw calm water around the boat and birds flying in the air. Add sea creatures beneath the water, like fish, more sea turtles, and corals. You can even add a sunken treasure or shipwreck!

LEARN IT! It's easy to feel overwhelmed when we have "storms" in our lives, isn't it? You might feel angry, scared, or frustrated when things don't go your way.

Psalm 107:23-32 describes sailors in the middle of a BIG storm. *(For full context, read this passage with your children.)* The sailors were incredibly scared. Knowing they needed God's help, verse 28 says, "They cried out to the Lord." God heard their cries and stopped the storm. He made the water calm, just like the water in our pictures.

Not only did He stop the storm, but verse 25 says that God is the one who actually created the storm. We don't know why He wanted the sailors to go through the storm, but since God is trustworthy, we know He allowed the storm for a good reason.

DISCUSS IT! What's a problem that you've had recently? How did you try to fix it? What did the sailors do when they needed help? How did God help them? Why do you think God may have wanted them to experience the storm?

LIVE IT! When we go through something that seems overwhelming, scary, or just plain hard, we can trust that our good God allowed it, and we should ask Him to help us, just like the sailors did. He might not take away the hard thing as He did for the sailors, but He can calm the "storms" in our hearts by giving us peace, joy, and comfort. All we have to do is call on Him to help us and trust in Him.

Let's pray together now, praising God for His power to calm any storm and asking Him to comfort and help us during the "storms" we go through.

STUDY IT! For more confirmation on God being our helper, check out Psalm 46. To read about Jesus calming a raging storm, check out Luke 8:22-24.

MEMORIZE IT!

"The words of thoughtless people cut like swords.
But the tongue of wise people brings healing."

Proverbs 12:18 (NIRV)

DRAW IT! These knights are ready for battle! Add sharp swords to their hands and draw designs on their shields. You can also add some surrounding plants to the picture.

LEARN IT! Did you know that the words we say are very powerful? It's easy to think our words don't affect others very much. But Proverbs 12:18 teaches us that our words either hurt or help people.

Our words can be hurtful when we speak thoughtlessly. Thoughtless words are words we say without paying attention to how they make someone else feel. For example, imagine you spent time drawing a nice picture and showed it to a friend, just for them to say, "That doesn't look very good." How would your friend's thoughtless words make you feel? Thoughtless words don't just make people feel sad; thoughtless words cut like swords—they hurt people's hearts!

On the other hand, a wise person can actually heal hearts and relationships with their words...or with no words at all! Sometimes saying nothing is the best use of your tongue, and other times speaking comforting, loving, or encouraging words is best. Wise people think before they talk and only say words that are helpful to others.

DISCUSS IT! What kinds of words do you think would be considered "thoughtless?" How do thoughtless words compare to a sharp sword? What words would be considered "healing?" Can you give an example of when saying nothing at all would be the best use of your tongue?

LIVE IT! It's easy to say words without thinking, but in doing so, we risk hurting people with our thoughtless words, just like a sharp sword can hurt a knight in battle. We need God's help to be wise with our tongues so that we can bring healing to people instead.

Let's pray together now, asking God to help us say wise, not thoughtless, words when we speak to others.

STUDY IT! To learn more about controlling what you say, check out James 1:26-27 and Proverbs 10:19.

MEMORIZE IT!

"I will praise the name of God with a song; I will magnify him with thanksgiving."

Psalm 69:30 (ESV)

DRAW IT!   This "Thankfulness Telescope" is pretty special. When you write or draw what you're thankful for on it, you can see God more clearly! Write or draw what you're thankful for on the side of the telescope. Next, write "God" or draw a picture of what you think God may look like in the center of the lens.

LEARN IT!   It's easy to focus on things we don't like about our lives, isn't it? You may feel like complaining when you have to do chores instead of playing with friends or when you have to eat chicken for dinner instead of pizza.

Psalm 69:30 teaches us the power of thankfulness. When we tell God what we're thankful for, we see His greatness more clearly—we magnify Him in our hearts! Just like the huge moon looks small to us on earth but can be magnified through a telescope, so our huge God can seem small to us but can be magnified through our thankfulness. Thanking God helps us see how great He is because we are focusing on the truth of who He is and how much He has done for us.

Thanksgiving means to give thanks; it's saying what you're thankful for! When you're grumbling and complaining, the focus is on you and what you want. But when you tell God what you're thankful for and notice the good things He has given you and done for you, then it puts the focus on God. And when we tell others what we're thankful for, it helps them see God's greatness more clearly, too.

DISCUSS IT!   What's something that happened today that you're thankful for? How is thankfulness like a telescope? Why is it important to magnify God?

LIVE IT!   Thankfulness isn't always easy, but if we want to see the greatness of God clearly, then being thankful is a must! Each day this week, let's tell each other (or a friend) three things we're thankful for. Here are a few ideas to get us thinking—we can be thankful that God loves us so much that He sent Jesus to die for us, we can be thankful for our family, and we can be thankful for our home.

Let's pray together now, asking God to help us magnify Him with thanksgiving and to help us not complain.

STUDY IT!   Check out Luke 17:11-19 to learn more about the power of thankfulness.

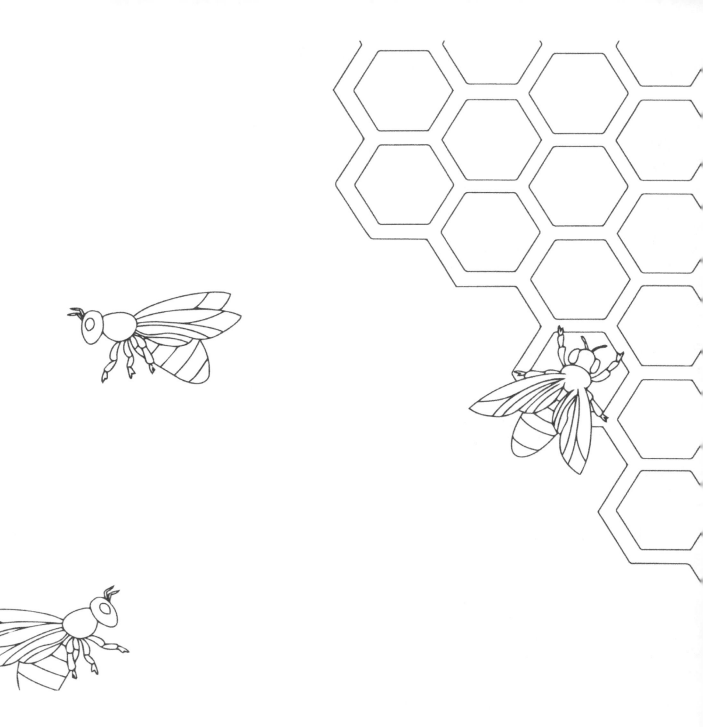

Memorize It!

"Pleasant words are a honeycomb, sweet to the soul and healing to the bones."

Proverbs 16:24 (NASB)

WEEK 18

DRAW IT! Honey is a sweet, sticky treat that even people in the Bible enjoyed eating. Draw some honey dripping from the honeycomb. Add a lot of surrounding bees, too!

LEARN IT! Eating a favorite dessert makes us feel happy, doesn't it? In Bible times, honey was a common dessert. You might not eat a lot of honey, but you probably get pretty excited when you get to have a sweet treat! Eating honey or another type of sugar can cheer us up when we're feeling down. Proverbs 16:24 teaches us that pleasant words do the same thing.

Just like honey or another dessert makes you happy, pleasant words spoken to you can make you feel happy too. Pleasant words are gracious, kind, and good words. They're words spoken to brighten our day, cheer us up, and encourage us. The opposite of pleasant words would be bad, ugly, mean words—words that make people feel frustrated, hurt, and discouraged.

For example, if you just lost a basketball game, and someone said to you, "Your team lost big time! You didn't play very well," then you would feel worse because of their hurtful words. On the other hand, if after the same game, someone said, "I loved watching you play; you really tried your best out there!" then you would feel a little better about losing the game. Their pleasant words would bring sweetness to your heart, just as if you had eaten a bit of honey!

DISCUSS IT! What is your favorite sweet treat to eat? How do you feel when you're eating it? How are pleasant words like eating a sweet treat? Can you think of a time when someone spoke pleasant words to you?

LIVE IT! Pleasant words have the power to help others feel good. We'd much rather people speak to us with kind, good words, so let's make it our goal to speak that way to them too.

Let's pray now, asking God to help us speak kind, not hurtful, words to others.

STUDY IT! To learn more about the power of words, check out James 3:1-12.

Memorize It!

"Look at the birds of the air. They don't plant or gather crops.
They don't put away crops in storerooms.
But your Father who is in heaven feeds them.
Aren't you worth much more than they are?
Can you add even one hour to your life by worrying?...
But put God's kingdom first. Do what he wants you to do.
Then all those things will also be given to you."

Matthew 6:26-27, 33 (NIRV)

DRAW IT! These birds look hungry! Add some more fish to the water for them to eat. Also, draw some fruit trees and berry bushes.

LEARN IT! In this verse, Jesus is talking to a group of people about the sin of worrying. Worrying means you are afraid that you won't get the things you want or think you need. Worrying is a sign that you're not trusting God. In these verses, Jesus is teaching people how important it is to trust God, and He's using nature as an example.

God is the one that takes care of the birds and other animals. He makes sure they have what they need to live in the wild. Jesus tells the people that they are more important to God than a bird, so they can trust God will provide for their needs too. This doesn't mean they'll always get exactly what they want or think they need. Sometimes what people think they need doesn't line up with what God knows they need. But Jesus lets the people know that God is a good God they can trust to care for them.

Instead of worrying, Jesus tells the people to "put God's kingdom first. Do what he wants you to do." Like a hungry bird might chase after an insect to eat, so Jesus wants us to chase after God and obedience to Him more than anything else.

DISCUSS IT! Can you think of examples of how God cares for wild animals? What does it mean to worry? Why shouldn't we worry? What does the verse say we should do instead of worrying?

LIVE IT! Let's take time this week to explore nature together. Let's write down a list of all the animals we see and note how God cares for them.

Just like wild animals can trust God to give them what they need, so we can trust Him to provide what we need. Let's pray together now, thanking God for caring for us. Let's also ask God to help us chase after His kingdom and obedience to Him.

STUDY IT! Read Genesis 21:14-20 to learn how God cared for a mother and son.

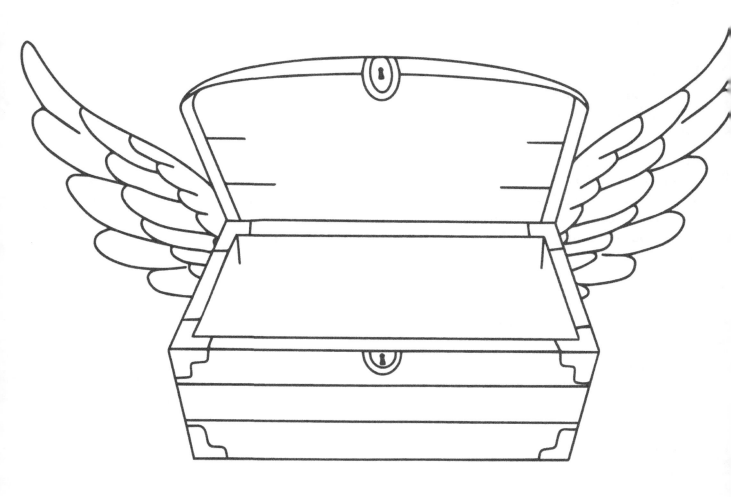

Memorize It!

"Cast but a glance at riches, and they are gone, for they will surely sprout wings and fly off to the sky like an eagle."

Proverbs 23:5 (NIV)

DRAW IT! This empty treasure chest needs to be filled up. Usually, a treasure chest holds valuable things, like diamonds, gold coins, and jewelry. If this was your treasure chest, what special things of yours would you put inside it? Would you fill it with video games, money, or something else? Draw what you value inside the treasure chest.

LEARN IT! What did you draw inside the treasure chest? Those things must be very important to you! Now, imagine your treasure chest picture flying off into the sky with all of your valuable things inside it. This is the picture Proverbs 23:5 is painting for us. It's teaching us that the things we own will not be around forever. Even though it's fun to get new things like games, dolls, and even money, none of these things were made to last.

DISCUSS IT! What's a toy you've had that's gotten lost or broken? Why do you think it didn't last forever?

LIVE IT! This week, when you're playing, try to think of the treasure chest picture you drew. Your toys may eventually break, get lost, or you may just lose interest in them. They won't always be with you. It's ok to enjoy your stuff, but only God and His kingdom last forever.

God loves us so much that He sent His Son, Jesus, to die for us, so our sins can be forgiven and we can have a close relationship with Him. He doesn't want anything to come between Him and us; He wants us to love Him more than anything else.

Let's pray together now, asking God to help us remember that He, not our things, will always be with us. Let's also thank God for His forever love for us and ask Him to help us love Him more than any treasures we might get.

STUDY IT! Read Matthew 6:19-21 and 1 Timothy 6:17-19 to learn more about lasting, heavenly treasure.

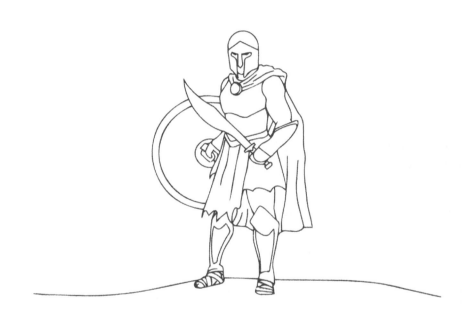

MEMORIZE IT!

"It is better to be patient than to fight.
It is better to control your temper than to take a city."

Proverbs 16:32 (NIRV)

WEEK 21

DRAW IT! That warrior just captured a city all by himself! Draw city buildings around him. Put a pile of treasure by his feet that he stole from the people of the city.

LEARN IT! How does the warrior look? He just conquered that city, so he must be strong and brave, right? While big, muscular men appear great and powerful, Proverbs 16:32 teaches us that a patient, self-controlled person is actually better in God's eyes than a strong warrior.

But being self-controlled and patient can be difficult. It's easy to shout and show our frustration when things don't go our way. Just think about when a sibling is annoying you. You might want to say angry words and try to "overtake" them (like the warrior in the verse) rather than respond in patience and self-control.

Anyone can get big, strong muscles if they exercise their bodies the right way. But God would rather us have spiritual "muscles," like patience and self-control. To get these muscles, it takes a different kind of strength—the strength of telling God that you need His help and letting Him change your thoughts, wants, and feelings to be like His. When we do that, He is sure to help us be spiritually strong, which is better than the strength of a warrior.

DISCUSS IT! What spiritual strengths are mentioned in the verse? Why is a patient, self-controlled person better than a warrior who fights? How do we become patient and self-controlled?

LIVE IT! When life gets difficult, it's easy to be out of control and impatient. But God wants you to be greater than a warrior by being patient and self-controlled.

Let's pray now for God to give us patience and self-control when we feel angry, discouraged, or disappointed. Only through the help of His Spirit can our hearts change to be the way He wants them to be.

STUDY IT! To learn more about how God changes His followers to be like Him, check out 2 Peter 1:3-11.

Memorize It!

"If any of you lacks wisdom, let him ask God, who gives generously to all without reproach, and it will be given him. But let him ask in faith, with no doubting, for the one who doubts is like a wave of the sea that is driven and tossed by the wind."

James 1:5-6 (ESV)

DRAW IT! Imagine there's a big thunderstorm going through the picture. Draw huge storm clouds, lots of rain, and bright lightning. Be sure to add crashing waves!

LEARN IT! Do the waves in our pictures look calm and peaceful? No way! They're out of control, blown back and forth, up and down. They're going wherever the wind takes them.

Doubting God means trusting ourselves instead of Him. It's believing that we know what's best for us better than He does. When we doubt God, we'll be like the waves in the picture, unsteady and without peace.

Instead of doubting, we should ask God in faith for what we want. Asking in faith means we trust God no matter how He answers our prayers. The person who prays in faith says, "God, this is what I want. If I don't get it, I'll believe that that's what's best for me. I'll trust You no matter what."

DISCUSS IT! How is doubting God like being a wave during a storm? What does it mean to ask in faith?

LIVE IT! Let's now practice praying in faith by asking God for something we want but are unsure if it's what He wants us to have. Maybe you want to win the next game you play with a sibling, or perhaps you want a new toy. Those things may seem good to you, but God might not want you to have them for some reason. What would you like to pray in faith about?

Let's also ask God for something we know He wants us to have. What's something God wants us to have? (Hint: see verse 5) God desires for us to have wisdom, so let's ask in faith for God to give that to us.

STUDY IT! To learn more about praying in faith, read Matthew 26:36-46 and discover how Jesus prayed in faith before He died on the cross.

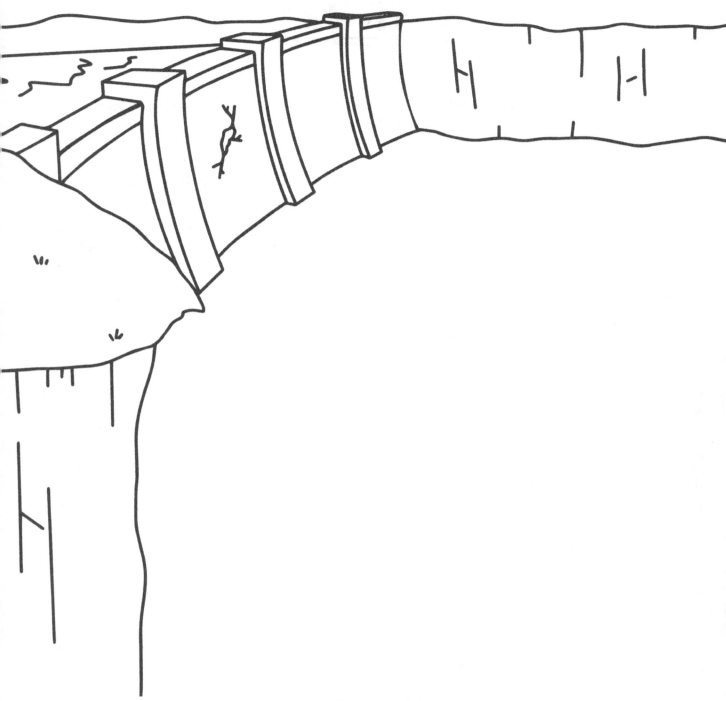

MEMORIZE IT!

"Starting to argue is like making a crack in a dam.
So drop the matter before a fight breaks out."

Proverbs 17:14 (NIRV)

DRAW IT!   Oh no! There's a crack in the dam! This is a big problem. Draw water pouring out of the crack. Add a town in front of the dam that the rushing water will destroy.

LEARN IT!   Can you imagine if a real dam cracked open and the water it was holding back flooded out onto the ground beneath it? The water would destroy everything in its path!

When things don't go our way, it's easy to want to fight with other people, arguing with them to get what we want. But Proverbs 17:14 teaches us that starting an argument is just like making a crack in a dam. When we begin to argue, we release our own type of flood—a flood of hurtful words and actions that flow from anger, selfishness, and pride. Nothing good will come from this type of flood. It will destroy relationships, just like the floods in our pictures are destroying the towns we drew.

Instead of fighting, this verse tells us to "drop the matter." Dropping the matter means to stop talking about the thing that is causing the argument. For example, maybe you and a sibling want to play with the same toy. Instead of beginning to argue about it, you can choose to say, "You can have it first. I'll take a turn later." That's dropping the matter. Doing this will bring peace to your house, love to your sibling, and glory to God.

DISCUSS IT!   What would happen if a dam broke near our house and water came rushing down our street? How does flood water destroying a town compare to an argument destroying a relationship? What does it mean to "drop the matter?"

LIVE IT!   Let's ask God now to bring Proverbs 17:14 and the pictures we drew to our minds whenever we feel like arguing. Let's pray that He helps us remember that starting to argue is just like making a crack in a dam. Let's ask Him to help us drop the matter during those times of frustration instead.

STUDY IT!   To learn more about why people argue, read James 4:1-10 (note what verse 1 says).

Memorize It!

"The Lord and King gives me strength. He makes my feet like the feet of a deer. He helps me walk on the highest places."

Habakkuk 3:19 (NIRV)

WEEK 24

DRAW IT! That deer needs some ground under him! Draw a tall mountain below the deer. Also add wildflowers, rabbits, and pine trees to the picture.

LEARN IT! The book of Habakkuk is a conversation between the prophet Habakkuk and God. In short, Habakkuk is asking God why so many bad things are happening in his life. Do you ever wonder that?

Maybe a family member is very sick and isn't getting better. Or maybe your best friend moved away, and you don't get to play with him anymore. We all have to go through hard things, and when life isn't going well, it's easy to wonder why God doesn't fix our problems. Habakkuk had these thoughts too. God answered Habakkuk by reminding him that He is a good God and Habakkuk can and should trust Him, even when it's difficult.

The words in Habakkuk 3:19 are Habakkuk's final response to God and the last verse of the book. By the end of the book, Habakkuk recognized that God was the "Lord and King," and he pictured himself like a deer climbing tall mountains because the Lord gave him strength.

DISCUSS IT! What's the highest place you've ever been? The book of Habakkuk is a conversation between who? What was Habakkuk asking God? How does remembering that God is the "Lord and King" help us when bad things happen?

LIVE IT! Do you ever feel sad and wonder why God doesn't make things better in your life? It's normal to feel that way; even Habakkuk felt like that. But we can trust that God is good even when life gets tough. And God will give us strength for life's challenges, just like He gave Habakkuk.

Let's pray now, asking God to give us strength, so we can climb the difficult "mountains" of our lives, just as if we were a strong and graceful deer.

STUDY IT! For the full context of this verse, read the whole book of Habakkuk, and note the back and forth conversation between Habakkuk and God.

53

Extra Illustrations

These pages are specifically designed to be removed from the book and displayed after your children embellish them according to the week's instructions.

Memorize It!

"The heavens declare the glory of God; the skies proclaim the work of his hands."
Psalm 19:1 (NIV)

Memorize It!

"When I remember you on my bed, I meditate on you in the night watches, For you have been my help, and in the shadow of your wings I sing for joy."
Psalm 63:6-7 (NASB)

59

Memorize It!

"The path of the righteous is like the morning sun, shining ever brighter till the full light of day. But the way of the wicked is like deep darkness; they do not know what makes them stumble."

Proverbs 4:18-19 (NIV)

MEMORIZE IT!

"You are my hiding place; you will protect me from trouble and surround me with songs of deliverance."

Psalm 32:7 (NIV)

Memorize It!

"When you pass through the waters, I will be with you; and when you pass through the rivers, they will not sweep over you... For I am the Lord your God, the Holy One of Israel, your Savior."

Isaiah 43:2a, 3a (NIV)

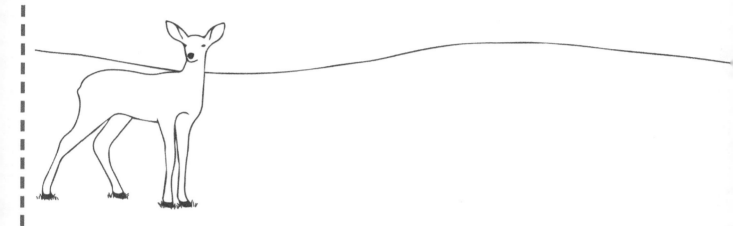

Memorize It!

"A deer longs for streams of water. God, I long for you in the same way."

Psalm 42:1 (NIRV)

Memorize It!

"My sheep listen to my voice. I know them, and they follow me."

John 10:27 (NIRV)

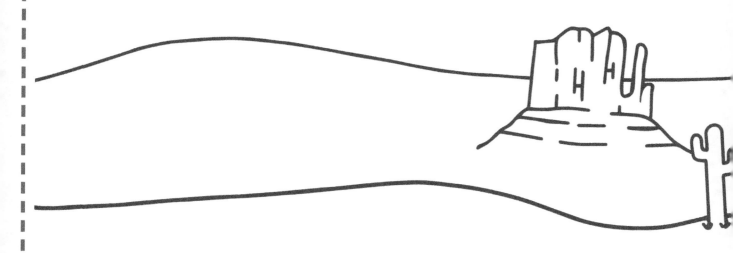

Memorize It!

"This is what the LORD says: 'Cursed is the man who trusts in mankind and makes flesh his strength, and whose heart turns away from the LORD. For he will be like a bush in the desert, and will not see when prosperity comes."

Jeremiah 17:5-6a (NASB)

Memorize It!

"Blessed is the man who trusts in the Lord, and whose trust is the Lord. For he will be like a tree planted by the water that extends its roots by a stream, and does not fear when the heat comes; but its leaves will be green, and it will not be anxious in a year of drought, nor cease to yield fruit."

Jeremiah 17:7-8 (NASB)

MEMORIZE IT!

"Therefore everyone who hears these words of mine and puts them into practice is like a wise man who built his house on the rock...
But everyone who hears these words of mine and does not put them into practice is like a foolish man who built his house on sand."

Matthew 7:24, 26 (NIV)

75

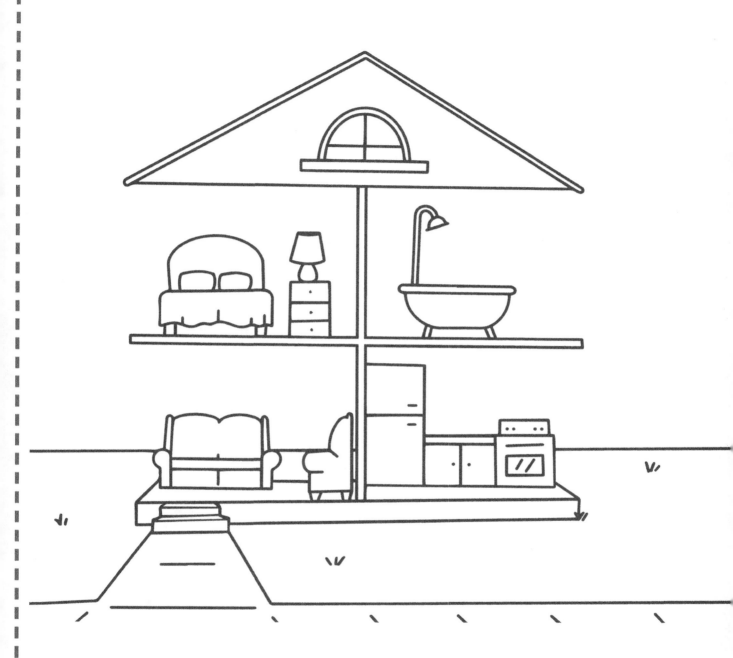

Memorize It!

"A man without self-control is like a city broken into and left without walls."
Proverbs 25:28 (ESV)

77

Memorize It!

"Even youths grow tired and weary, and young men stumble and fall; but those who hope in the Lord will renew their strength. They will soar on wings like eagles; they will run and not grow weary, they will walk and not be faint."

Isaiah 40:30-31 (NIV)

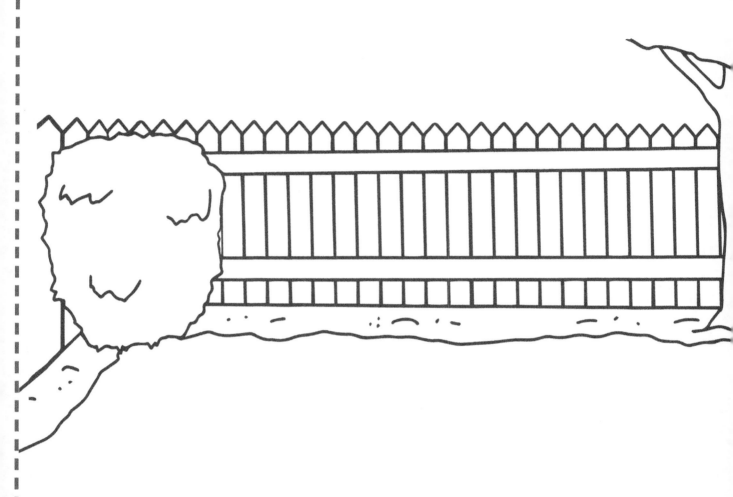

Memorize It!

"A gentle answer turns anger away. But mean words stir up anger."

Proverbs 15:1 (NIRV)

Memorize It!

"At one time my heart was sad and my spirit was bitter. I didn't have any sense.
I didn't know anything. I acted like a wild animal toward you.
But I am always with you. You hold me by my right hand."

Psalm 73:21-23 (NIRV)

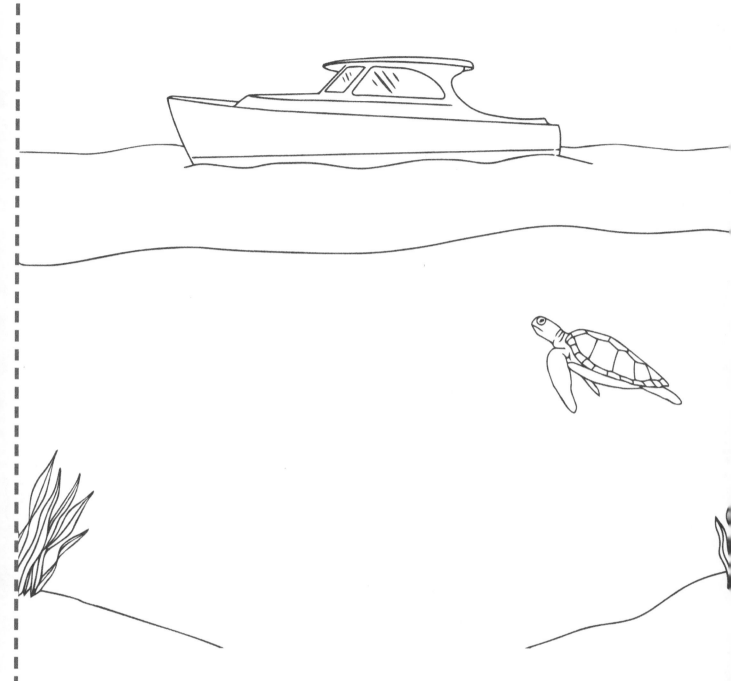

Memorize It!

"Then they cried out to the Lord because of their problems. And he brought them out of their troubles. He made the storm as quiet as a whisper. The waves of the ocean calmed down."

Psalm 107:28-29 (NIRV)

MEMORIZE IT!

"The words of thoughtless people cut like swords.
But the tongue of wise people brings healing."

Proverbs 12:18 (NIRV)

Memorize It!

"I will praise the name of God with a song; I will magnify him with thanksgiving."

Psalm 69:30 (ESV)

89

Memorize It!

"Pleasant words are a honeycomb, sweet to the soul and healing to the bones."

Proverbs 16:24 (NASB)

Memorize It!

"Look at the birds of the air. They don't plant or gather crops.
They don't put away crops in storerooms.
But your Father who is in heaven feeds them.
Aren't you worth much more than they are?
Can you add even one hour to your life by worrying?...
But put God's kingdom first. Do what he wants you to do.
Then all those things will also be given to you."

Matthew 6:26-27, 33 (NIRV)

93

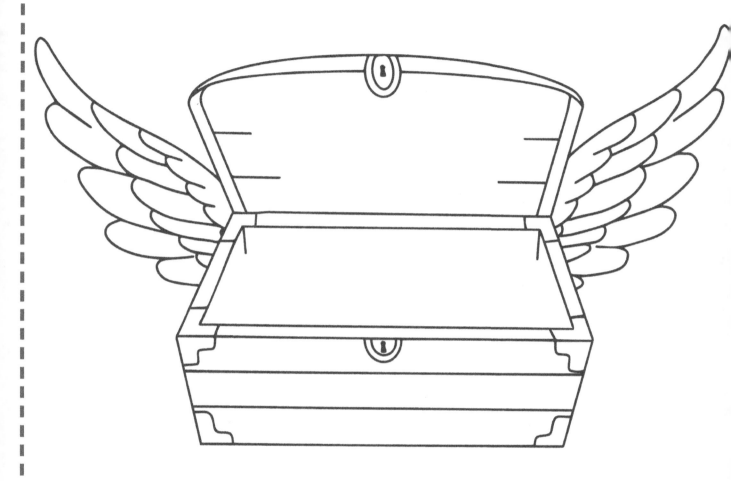

MEMORIZE IT!

"Cast but a glance at riches, and they are gone, for they will surely sprout wings and fly off to the sky like an eagle."

Proverbs 23:5 (NIV)

Memorize It!

"It is better to be patient than to fight.
It is better to control your temper than to take a city."

Proverbs 16:32 (NIRV)

Memorize It!

"If any of you lacks wisdom, let him ask God, who gives generously to all
without reproach, and it will be given him. But let him ask in faith,
with no doubting, for the one who doubts is like a wave
of the sea that is driven and tossed by the wind."

James 1:5-6 (ESV)

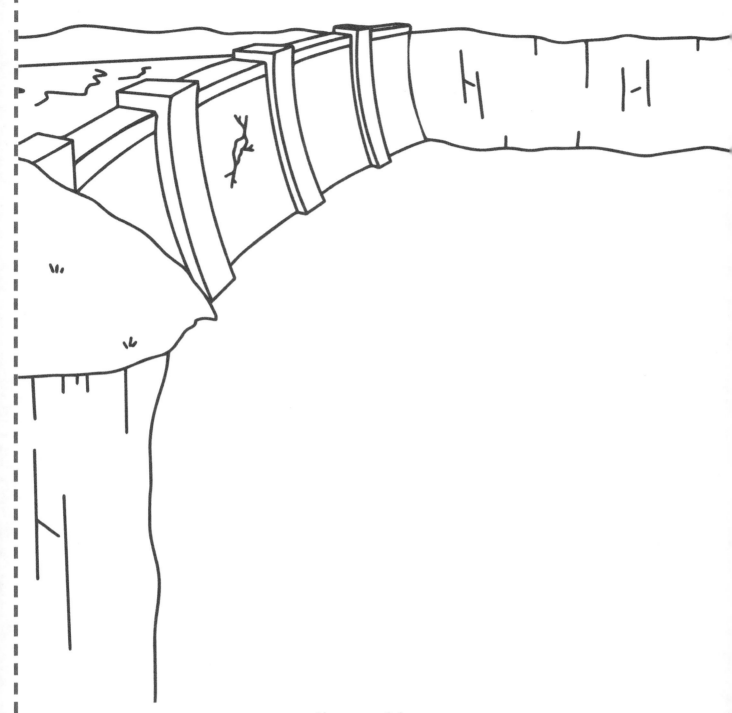

Memorize It!

"Starting to argue is like making a crack in a dam.
So drop the matter before a fight breaks out."

Proverbs 17:14 (NIRV)

Memorize It!

"The Lord and King gives me strength. He makes my feet like the feet of a deer. He helps me walk on the highest places."

Habakkuk 3:19 (NIRV)

Made in the USA
Las Vegas, NV
17 July 2024

92459921R00059